$\mathcal{I}$ntroduction

Red Wing Potteries made beautiful, stylish dinnerware from 1935 until it closed in 1967. Initial offerings were bright, solid-colored pieces that preceded Fiesta Ware, one of the most well known dinnerware brands of the era. Through the 40s, 50s and 60s, hand-painted patterns predominated at Red Wing. In 1967, when the company closed, it was the only commercial pottery manufacturer in the United States still hand-painting dinnerware.

This price guide gives you the basic tools for identifying and pricing your dinnerware. Most of the Red Wing dinnerware patterns belong to a specific line or shape, such as the Concord Line. Each line consists of a number of pieces that make up a set of dinnerware, and each set was offered in a variety of patterns (with a few exceptions, such as the Town & Country Line, which was only offered in one pattern but in nine different colors). In this guide, we have arranged the dinnerware according to each line in approximately the same order that the line was first introduced.

A variety of collectors and dealers consulted on the prices in this guide. The values given are only to be used as a suggestion, not a definitive price structure. Prices are based on pieces in **PERFECT CONDITION**, meaning pieces without chips, cracks, crazing, stains or heavy wear. Keep in mind that prices vary throughout the country and can go up (or down) with time. Please use your own discretion as to the value of Red Wing dinnerware. If a piece is not in this book, it does not necessarily make it rare or valuable because dinnerware lines were always changing, and new pieces were constantly being added or discontinued. The author assumes no responsibility for the use of this price guide.

Many thanks to my staff Tom Rostowski, Maureen O'Meara Follis and Gretchen Larsen. Thanks also to Scott Gillmer and Red Wing Pottery Sales, as well as Kirsten Ulve, Dan Ciampaglia, Claudia Parrish, Dan Follis and Christine Boos. A big thanks to my consultants Mary Bang, Cliff Ekdahl, Jan and Al of Hill Street Antiques and Curtis Johnson. Additional thanks to Arlone Crowson and Pottery Place Antique Shop, Colleen and Ernie Nelson and Al Novek. I also would like to thank Stan Bougie and Dave Newkirk for creating the first book on Red Wing Dinnerware.

Most importantly, special thanks to all the people who worked so hard, some their entire lives, to produce this dinnerware for all of us to enjoy.

Special thanks also to Curtis Johnson for allowing us to photograph his pieces for the front cover.

RED WING ART POTTERY Including Pottery Made For RumRill by Ray Reiss is the definitive book for information on Red Wing art pottery, kitchenware, cookie jars, lamps and specialty items. This beautiful 240-page coffee table book contains more than 800 color photographs as well as an accurate price guide.

Information on ordering additional copies of this *Red Wing Dinnerware Price and Identification Guide*, and other quality Red Wing books, is on the inside back cover.

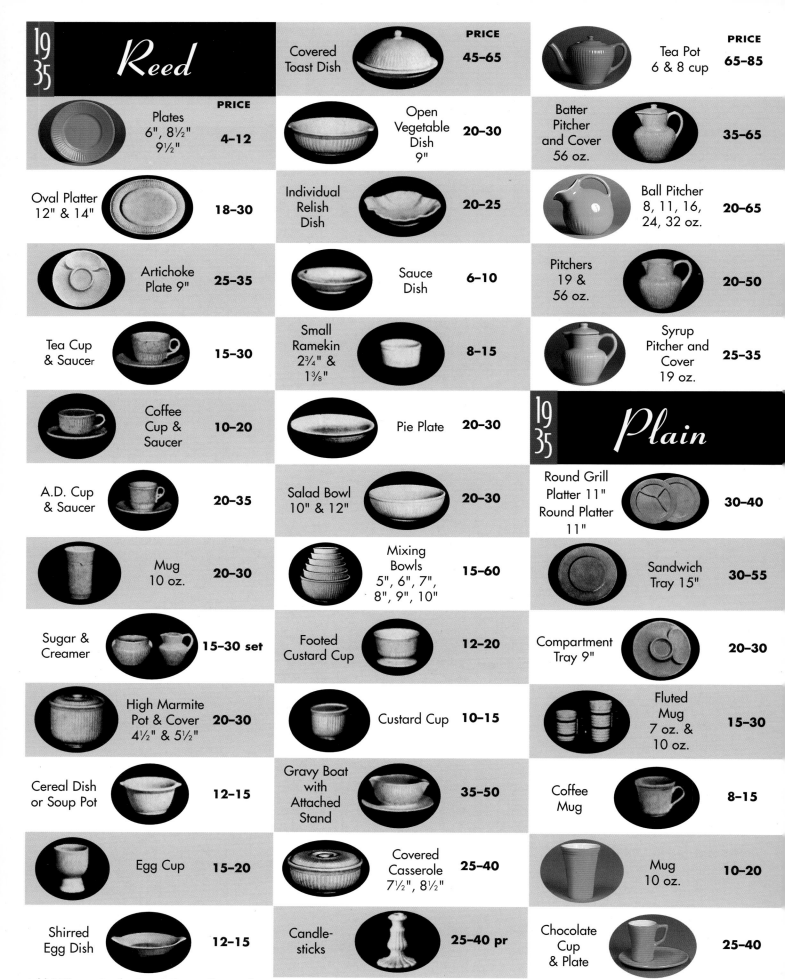

1935 Reed

Item	Price
Plates 6", 8½", 9½"	4–12
Oval Platter 12" & 14"	18–30
Artichoke Plate 9"	25–35
Tea Cup & Saucer	15–30
Coffee Cup & Saucer	10–20
A.D. Cup & Saucer	20–35
Mug 10 oz.	20–30
Sugar & Creamer	15–30 set
High Marmite Pot & Cover 4½" & 5½"	20–30
Cereal Dish or Soup Pot	12–15
Egg Cup	15–20
Shirred Egg Dish	12–15

Item	Price
Covered Toast Dish	45–65
Open Vegetable Dish 9"	20–30
Individual Relish Dish	20–25
Sauce Dish	6–10
Small Ramekin 2¾" & 1⅜"	8–15
Pie Plate	20–30
Salad Bowl 10" & 12"	20–30
Mixing Bowls 5", 6", 7", 8", 9", 10"	15–60
Footed Custard Cup	12–20
Custard Cup	10–15
Gravy Boat with Attached Stand	35–50
Covered Casserole 7½", 8½"	25–40
Candle-sticks	25–40 pr

Item	Price
Tea Pot 6 & 8 cup	65–85
Batter Pitcher and Cover 56 oz.	35–65
Ball Pitcher 8, 11, 16, 24, 32 oz.	20–65
Pitchers 19 & 56 oz.	20–50
Syrup Pitcher and Cover 19 oz.	25–35

1935 Plain

Item	Price
Round Grill Platter 11" Round Platter 11"	30–40
Sandwich Tray 15"	30–55
Compartment Tray 9"	20–30
Fluted Mug 7 oz. & 10 oz.	15–30
Coffee Mug	8–15
Mug 10 oz.	10–20
Chocolate Cup & Plate	25–40

Add 25% to price for Royal Blue. Yellow and Orange are at the higher end of the price range while Ivory and Turquoise are at the lower end.

	PRICE			PRICE			PRICE

Sugar & Creamer — **20–35 set**

French Design Pitcher 8, 12, 16 oz. — **15–45**

Tea Cup & Saucer — **15–25**

Sugar & Creamer — **10–20 set**

Jug with Ice Stop 64 oz. — **25–45**

A.D. Cup & Saucer — **25–35**

Salt & Pepper — **15–25 pr**

Swirl Pitcher 64 oz. — **35–65**

Sugar & Creamer — **25–35 set**

French Marmite Pot & Cover 4½" — **15–25**

Batter Pitcher — **25–35**

Range Salt & Pepper — **25–35 pr**

Low Marmite Pot and Cover 4½", 5½" — **12–20**

Coffee Server & Cover — **25–35**

Open Vegetable Dish 9" — **25–35**

Oil Cruet — **25–35**

Syrup Jug & Cover — **20–30**

Cereal Dish or Soup Pot — **15–25**

Mustard & Cover — **15–20**

Monastery Jug 8 & 16 oz. — **20–35**

Footed Custard Cup — **18–25**

Chili Bowl 5" — **12–20**

Individual Coffee Server & Cover — **25–35**

Ash Tray — **15–25**

Boston Baked Bean Pot & Cover 15, 23, 32 oz. — **15–30**

19 36 *Chevron*

Kettle Flower Vase 3" Kettle Candlestick 3" (shown) — **15–25**

Ball Cookie Jar 7" & 8" — **60–90**

Plates 6", 7", 8", 10", 12" — **6–20**

Range Jar with Cover — **20–30**

Ashtray 4½" — **12–18**

Oval Platters 12" & 14" — **20–30**

Tea Pot 6 cup — **45–75**

Duck Ashtray — **35–65**

Sandwich Tray 15" — **35–50**

A.D. Coffee Pot — **75–100**

Ice Tub 6" — **50–75**

Grill Plate 11" — **20–30**

Pitcher 19 & 32 oz. — **25–45**

Pitcher with Ice Stop 70 oz.	**PRICE** 45–75	Chop Plate 30–45
Cocktail Jug 6 pint	125–150	Tea Cup & Saucer 20–30
Cocktail Cup	20–35	Mug 7 & 10 oz. 12–20

19 37 *Ivanhoe*

Plates	**PRICE** rare
Cup & Saucer	30–45
Sugar	20–30
Creamer	20–30
Salt & Pepper	25–45 pr
Pitcher	45–65

19 38 *Fondoso*

Plates 6½", 8½", 9½", 12"	8–15
Oval Platter 12"	30–45

Small Sugar & Creamer	25–35 set
Large Sugar & Creamer	30–45 set
Small Salt & Pepper	20–30 pr
Large Salt & Pepper	30–40 pr
Covered Butter Dish	50–75
French Marmite Pot & Cover 4½"	15–25
Low Marmite Pot & Cover 4½"	12–20
Soup or Cereal Dish	15–20
Shirred Egg Dish	15–20
Coupe Soup Dish 7½"	12–20

	PRICE
Vegetable Dish	18–25
Relish Dish	25–30
Sauce Dish	8–12
Salad Bowl	25–40
Mixing Bowls 5", 6", 7", 8", 9"	20–40 ea
Custard Cup	15–20
Dessert Cup	18–25
Covered Casserole 8½"	40–85
Cookie Jar and Cover 8½"	125–150
Jar for Sugar 8½" Capacity 5 lbs.	50–75
Jar for Flour 8½" Capacity 3½ lbs.	50–75
Jar for Coffee 8½" Capacity 2 lbs.	50–75
Tea Pot 3 & 6 cup	35–75

Fondoso available in Yellow, Orange, Turquoise, Pastel Green, Pastel Blue, Pastel Pink and Pastel Yellow.

		PRICE
	Coffee Pot	50–75
	Coffee Server (with Wood Handle)	30–45
	Tilt Pitcher	45–65
	Straight Pitcher	30–65
	Batter Pitcher and Cover	35–65
	Batter Pitcher Tray	25–35
	Syrup Jug and Cover	25–35

1942 Labriego
Later known as Hospitality Ware

	Plates 13" & 15"	rare
	Mug	25–35
	Sugar & Creamer	30–50 set
	Salt & Pepper	35–50 pr
	Oval Marmite & Cover	25–45

		PRICE
	Round Marmite with Cover	25–45
	Oval Casserole with French Handle 8" & 11"	45–85
	Oval Bean Pot with Cover 7"	30–50
	Tea Pot	75–100
	Coffee Server	50–75
	Water Pitcher	40–75
	Ashtray & Drink holder	rare

Labriego Ware

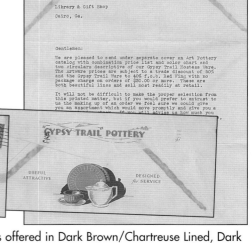

THE RED WING POTTERIES, INC.
MANUFACTURERS
Art Pottery · Food Containers · Flower Pots · Kitchen Ware
RED WING, MINNESOTA
Oct. 14, 1938

Library & Gift Shop
Cairo, Ga.

Gentlemen:

We are pleased to send under separate cover an Art Pottery catalog with combination price list and color chart and two circulars descriptive of our Gypsy Trail Hostess Ware. The Artware prices are subject to a trade discount of 50% and the Gypsy Trail Ware to 40% f.o.b. Red Wing with no package charge on orders of $50.00 or more. These are both beautiful lines and sell most readily at retail.

It will not be difficult to make the proper selection from this printed matter, but if you would prefer to entrust to us the making up of an order we feel sure we could give you an assortment which would move promptly and give you a ... if you will advise us how much you ...

Labriego Ware was offered in Dark Brown/Chartreuse Lined, Dark Brown/Orange, Gray/Maroon, Gray/Turquoise. Hospitality Ware was offered in Blue/White, Yellow/White, Green/Dark Brown and Beige/Dark Brown.

Provincial

SHAPE	Plates 6", 7", 10"	Chop Plate 12" & 14"	Tea Cup & Saucer	Sugar with Cover and Creamer	Salt & Pepper	Coupe Soup Bowl 8"	Cream Soup Bowl with Cover	Buffet Bowl
PATTERN								
Ardennes	8–20	30–45	15–20	25–30 ea	16–24 pr	15–20	30–35	40–50
Brittany	10–25	45–65	18–25	30–35 ea	20–36 pr	15–25	35–50	50–80
Orleans	10–25	45–65	18–25	30–35 ea	20–40 pr	15–25	40–55	60–90
Normandy*	8–20	40–60	15–20	25–30 ea	16–24 pr	15–20	30–35	50–80

*Normandy also was offered in a plain pattern with a striped edge.

SHAPE

Nappy 9"	Gravy Boat	Casserole without Cover (Vegetable Dish)	Covered Casserole	Candle Holders	Tea Pot with Cover	Water Jug	Beverage Server with Cover	PATTERN
20–28	30–40	15–25	45–65	45–65 pr	60–75	35–45	45–55	Ardennes
25–35	35–50	15–25	55–80	60–80 pr	80–120	50–85	60–85	Brittany
30–40	40–55	15–25	60–90	60–90 pr	85–125	60–90	65–95	Orleans
20–28	30–45	15–20	55–85	50–80 pr	75–100	45–75	50–80	Normandy

Normandy

THE NORMANDY pattern combines the charm of the Provincial shape with a decoration that is colorful and contemporary yet consistent. "When It's Apple Blossom Time in Normandy" is the inspiration. Like the Ardennes, this pattern is offered in a choice of two colors on the hollow ware—Dubonnet and Forest Green—harmonizing with the colors in the decoration on the flat ware and covers.

See reverse side for prices.

Orleans
PROVINCIAL LUNCHEON WARE

Concord

PATTERN	Plates 10½", 7½" & 6½"	Chop Plate	Supper Tray	Egg Plate with Cover	Tea Cup & Saucer	Coffee Cup	Sugar with Cover	Creamer	Salt & Pepper	Butter Dish with Cover	Spoon Rest	Cer Bo
Blossom Time	7–12	18–25	12–15	65–80	10–12	10–12	12–18	7–15	10–15 pr	18–25	10–20	7–1
Bud	rare	rare	rare	rare	rare	rare	rare	rare	rare	rare	rare	rar
Chrysanthemum	8–15	20–35	12–15	65–80	10–12	10–12	12–18	7–15	10–15 pr	18–25	10–20	7–1
Fantasy	12–25	30–45	15–20	80–100	12–15	12–15	15–25	12–15	15–20 pr	20–30	20–30	8–1
Fruit	12–25	30–45	18–25	75–95	12–15	12–15	12–18	12–15	15–20 pr	25–35	15–20	8–1
Harvest	15–100*	45–80	30–50	120–150	15–25	20–30	25–45	20–30	25–35 pr	40–60	30–50	18–3
Iris	12–25	30–45	18–25	75–95	10–15	10–12	12–18	12–15	12–18 pr	20–30	15–20	8–1
Lanterns	8–15	20–35	12–15	75–95	12–15	10–12	12–18	7–15	12–18 pr	20–30	15–20	8–1
Leaf Magic	15–45	–	–	–	–	–	–	–	–	–	–	–

*Plates from rare patterns such as Harvest Pattern are valued much higher than the rest of the line because many people collect only plates.

SHAPE

Cream Soup Bowl with Cover	Rim Soup	Divided Vegetable Dish	Relish Dish	Sauce or Fruit Dish	Celery Dish	Nappy	Gravy Boat with Tray	Casserole with Cover	Teapot & Cover	Water Pitcher	Beverage Server & Cover	PATTERN
12-15	7-12	15-25	15-20	5-7	15-20	12-15	15-25	25-35	45-60	25-45	45-60	Blossom Time
rare	rare	rare	rare	rare	rare	rare	rare	rare	rare	rare	rare	Bud
12-15	7-12	15-20	15-20	5-7	15-18	12-15	15-25	25-35	45-60	25-45	45-60	Chrysanthemum
15-20	10-15	20-25	20-25	10-20	25-35	18-25	20-35	35-45	60-85	30-55	60-80	Fantasy
15-20	10-15	20-25	20-25	6-8	18-20	18-25	20-35	35-45	60-85	30-55	60-80	Fruit
25-40	15-20	25-30	25-35	15-20	25-30	25-35	25-40	45-75	75-100	50-75	90-125	Harvest
15-20	10-15	20-25	20-25	6-8	18-20	18-25	20-35	35-45	60-85	30-55	60-80	Iris
15-20	10-15	20-25	20-25	6-8	18-20	15-25	20-35	35-45	50-75	30-55	60-80	Lanterns
-	-	-	-	-	-	-	-	-	-	-	-	Leaf Magic

Concord

PATTERN	Plates 10½", 7½" & 6½"	Chop Plate	Supper Tray	Egg Plate with Cover	Tea Cup & Saucer	Coffee Cup	Sugar with Cover	Creamer	Salt & Pepper	Butter Dish with Cover	Spoon Rest	Cer... Bo...
Lexington	7-12	18-25	12-15	65-85	10-12	10-12	12-18	7-12	10-15 pr	18-25	10-20	7-1
Lotus	8-15	20-35	12-15	75-95	10-12	10-12	12-18	7-15	10-15 pr	18-25	10-20	7-1
Magnolia	8-15	20-35	12-15	65-80	10-12	10-12	12-18	7-15	10-15 pr	18-25	10-20	7-1
Morning Glory Pink or Blue	8-15	20-35	12-15	75-95	10-12	10-12	12-18	7-15	10-15 pr	18-25	10-20	7-1
Nassau	15-40	35-50	30-45	85-110	15-25	15-20	20-35	20-30	25-35 pr	40-60	30-50	15-2
Quartette*	8-15	18-25	10-15	50-60	9-10	8-10	10-12	7-12	8-10 pr	15-20	10-15	6-8
Spring Song	10-20	20-35	15-20	75-95	10-12	10-12	12-18	12-15	12-18 pr	18-25	15-20	8-1
Willow Wind Pink or Blue	10-30	20-35	15-20	75-95	10-12	10-12	12-18	12-15	12-18 pr	18-25	15-20	8-1
Zinnia	15-60	35-50	30-40	85-110	15-25	15-20	20-35	20-30	25-35 pr	40-60	30-50	15-2

*Available in these colors: Mulberry, Chartreuse, Ming Green, and Copper Glow.

SHAPE

Cream Soup Bowl with Cover	Rim Soup Bowl	Divided Vegetable Dish	Relish Dish	Sauce or Fruit Dish	Celery Dish	Nappy	Gravy Boat with Tray	Casserole with Cover	Teapot & Cover	Water Pitcher	Beverage Server & Cover	PATTERN
2–15	7–12	15–20	15–20	5–7	15–18	12–15	15–25	25–35	45–60	25–45	45–60	Lexington
2–15	7–12	15–20	15–20	5–7	15–18	12–15	15–25	25–35	45–60	25–45	45–60	Lotus
2–15	7–12	15–20	15–20	5–7	15–18	12–15	15–25	25–35	45–60	25–45	45–60	Magnolia
2–15	7–12	15–20	15–20	6–8	18–20	18–20	15–25	25–35	60–85	30–45	45–60	Morning Glory Pink or Blue
0–35	15–20	25–30	25–30	12–18	20–30	25–35	25–40	40–60	75–100	50–75	85–100	Nassau
0–12	7–10	12–18	12–18	4–6	12–15	10–12	12–22	20–25	40–45	20–35	30–35	Quartette*
5–20	12–20	20–25	20–25	6–8	18–25	18–25	20–35	25–35	60–85	30–45	60–80	Spring Song
5–20	12–20	20–25	20–25	6–8	18–20	18–20	20–35	25–35	60–85	30–45	60–80	Willow Wind Pink or Blue
–35	15–20	25–30	25–30	12–18	20–30	25–35	25–40	40–60	75–100	50–75	85–100	Zinnia

Blossom Time

THE GAY COLORS of spring and summer blossom time radiate from this spritely pattern. Its informal charm lends excitement to any table setting whether modern or traditional.

The hollow ware is offered in matching glazes blending with the decorations of both flat ware and covers.

See reverse side for prices.

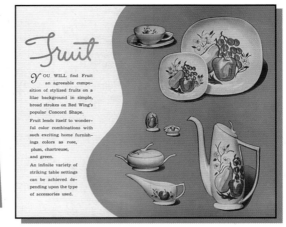

Fruit

YOU WILL find Fruit an agreeable composition of stylized fruits on a lilac background in simple, broad strokes on Red Wing's popular Concord Shape.

Fruit lends itself to wonderful color combinations with such exciting home furnishings colors as rose, plum, chartreuse, and green.

An infinite variety of striking table settings can be achieved depending upon the type of accessories used.

Magnolia

THE MAGNOLIA PATTERN is contemporary in design, reminiscent of the old South and Southern Hospitality. It lends itself equally well with the modern interiors of today or those of Period.

The hollow ware is offered in glazes—blending with the colors in the decoration of the flat ware and covers.

See reverse side for prices.

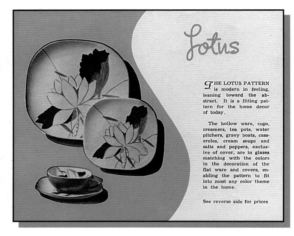

Lotus

THE LOTUS PATTERN is modern in feeling, leaning toward the abstract. It is a fitting pattern for the home decor of today.

The hollow ware, cups, creamers, tea pots, water pitchers, gravy boats, casseroles, cream soups and salts and peppers, exclusive of cover, are in glazes matching with the colors in the decoration of the flat ware and covers, enabling the pattern to fit into most any color theme in the home.

See reverse side for prices

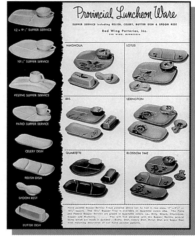

Morning Glory

THE MORNING-GLORY pattern carries a spring freshness. The flower is pink, leaves green.

The hollow ware is offered in two matching glazes—metallic brown and grey, blending with the colors in the decoration of the flat ware and covers.

See reverse side for prices.

Lanterns

LANTERNS is a delightful interpretation of a perennial favorite.

This beautifully hand painted design with a soft yellow background is on the popular square shape.

You will be pleased with the bold, rich, glowing colors and contemporary design.

Lanterns appeals equally to lovers of modern and those with a somewhat more conservative taste.

Dynasty DINNER WARE

SALT & PEPPER

TEA CUP & SAUCER

A. D. CUP & SAUCER

CASSEROLE WITH COVER

4 CUP TEAPOT & COVER

SAUCE OR FRUIT DISH

RIM SOUP

GRAVY BOAT

SUGAR WITH COVER

15" x 11" PLATTER

13" x 9 1/2" PLATTER

CREAM SOUP OR CEREAL

CREAMER

10 1/2" PLATE   9 1/2" PLATE   7 1/2" PLATE   6 1/2" PLATE

OPEN VEGETABLE

6 CUP TEAPOT & COVER

WATER PITCHER 20 OZ.

WATER PITCHER 40 OZ.

BEVERAGE SERVER & COVER

RED WING POTTERIES, INC., Red Wing, Minn.

RED WING PROVINCIAL COOKING WARE

Petite Marmites

Shirred Egg Dishes

Deep Casseroles

Shallow Casseroles

Oval Dishes

Bean Pots

Frying Pans

SEE OTH...

RED WING POTTERIES, ...

No.	Size	Capacity	Pot	Cover	Complete
28	6½"x 4½"	2 qt.	$13.20	$3.60	$16.80
29	7½"x 6"	4 "	28.50	4.50	33.00
30	8½"x 6½"	6 "	42.00	6.00	48.00

STOCK POT

Fancy Free DINNERWARE
RED WING POTTERY INC.
RED WING, MINNESOTA

SUGAR   CREAMER   CUP & SAUCER

SALT & PEPPER   CEREAL FRUIT   NAPPY   RIM SOUP   CASSEROLE & COVER

SUPPER TRAY

PLATE   10⅜" x 9¾"   7½" x 8¾"   6½" x 7¼"

TEA POT & COVER

GRAVY or SAUCE BOAT and TRAY

MARMITE & COVER

RELISH

DIVIDED VEGETABLE

BUTTER DISH

CELERY   PICKLE

PLATTER   EGG PLATE   WATER JUG   COFFEE SERVER & COVER

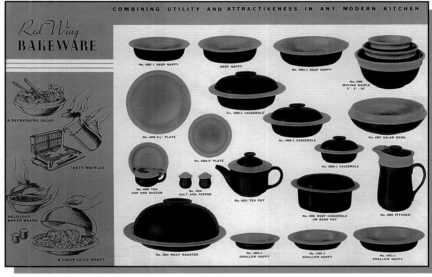

COMBINING UTILITY AND ATTRACTIVENESS IN ANY MODERN KITCHEN

Red Wing BAKEWARE

A REFRESHING SALAD

TASTY WAFFLES

DELICIOUS BAKED BEANS

A CRISP JUICY ROAST

No. 4003-1 DEEP NAPPY   DEEP NAPPY   No. 4002-3 DEEP NAPPY   No. 4006 MIXING BOWLS 6" - 8" - 10"

No. 4000-3 CASSEROLE

No. 4008-9½" PLATE

No. 4000-2 CASSEROLE

No. 4007 SALAD BOWL

No. 4008-6" PLATE

No. 4005 TEA CUP AND SAUCER

No. 4050 SALT & PEPPER

No. 4000-1 CASSEROLE

No. 4011 TEA POT

No. 4005 PITCHER

No. 4004 MEAT ROASTER

No. 4001 DEEP CASSEROLE OR BEAN POT

No. 4003-1 SHALLOW NAPPY

No. 4003-2 SHALLOW NAPPY

No. 4003-3 SHALLOW NAPPY

FRUIT OR SALAD SET

Party Ware

AN UNUSUAL, colorful and decorative group that will serve all occasions for informal entertaining, consisting of eight-inch plates, cups and saucers, large and individual salad bowls, party plate with cup, sandwich and relish dish.

1941 Provincial Cooking Ware

The Provincial Cooking Ware produced in 1941 differs from the 1963 Provincial Bakeware in that it is marked on the side of each piece. The Provincial made in 1963 is marked on the bottom.

Item		PRICE
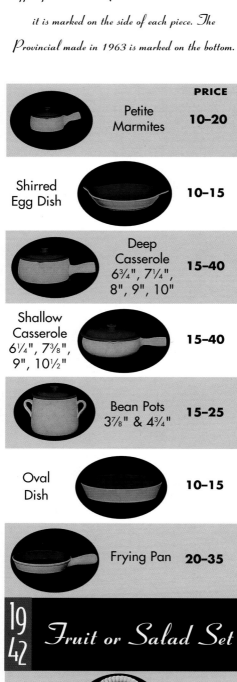 Petite Marmites		10–20
Shirred Egg Dish		10–15
Deep Casserole 6¾", 7¼", 8", 9", 10"		15–40
Shallow Casserole 6¼", 7⅜", 9", 10½"		15–40
Bean Pots 3⅞" & 4¾"		15–25
Oval Dish		10–15
Frying Pan		20–35

1942 Fruit or Salad Set

Item	PRICE
Bowl 12¾"	75–100
Individual Salad or Fruit Plate	20–40

1943 Party Ware or Fruit and Salad

Item	PRICE
Plates 8" & 11"	15–25
Sandwich Tray 13"	25–45
Cup for Party Plate	10–12
Saucer	10–15
Master Salad Bowl 13"	50–75
Individual Salad Bowl 6"	10–15
Celery Dish	35–50

1943 Bakeware

Item	PRICE
Plates	10–15
Tea Cup & Saucer	7–12
Salt & Pepper	10–20 pr
Salad Bowl	35–65

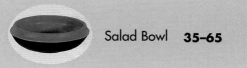

Item		PRICE
Mixing Bowls		20–40 ea
Deep Nappies 9"x7" 9½"x8" 11"x9"		15–25
Shallow Nappies 7"x5" 9"x7" 10½"x8½"		12–20
Deep Casserole with Cover (or Bean Pot) 10"x8½"		30–50
Shallow Casserole with Cover 7½"x5" 10"x8" 12"x10"		20–45
Meat Roaster with Cover		60–90
Tea Pot		50–75
Pitcher with Cover		45–65
Coffee Mug		10–15

1947 Town & Country

Item	Price
Soup Tureen & Ladle 	125–150
Casserole with Cover 	50–75
Plates 6½", 8", 12"	9–35*
Sauce or Relish Dish 7"x5", 9"x6"	10–18
Lazy Susan with Relish Dishes and Condiment Server or Mustard	150–200
Platter 15x11½" 11x7½"	35–60
Salad Spoon Right and Left 	rare
Tea Pot with Cover	110–125
Tea Cup & Saucer 	18–25
Coaster	15–20
Pitcher 2 & 3 pint	65–95
Mug	20–30
Baker 11"x7½" 	25–40
Syrup Jug	35–60
Sugar with Cover & Creamer	25–40 ea
Salt & Pepper 	40–75 pr
Marmite with Cover 	30–50
Condiment Server or Mustard (two parts)	60–80
Oil and Vinegar with Stoppers 	60–75 ea
Salad or Cereal Bowl 6", Salad Bowls 8½", 13"	18–65
Soup 7"	18–25
Mixing Bowl 9" 	60–80

*White plates $18–70

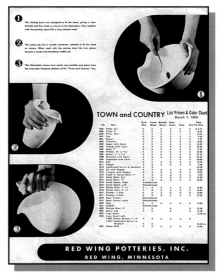

RED WING POTTERIES, INC.
RED WING, MINNESOTA

contemporary, functional

colorful, smart

15

Town & Country available in Dusk Blue, Forest Green, Metallic Brown, Chartreuse, Gray, Rust, Sand, Peach, and White.

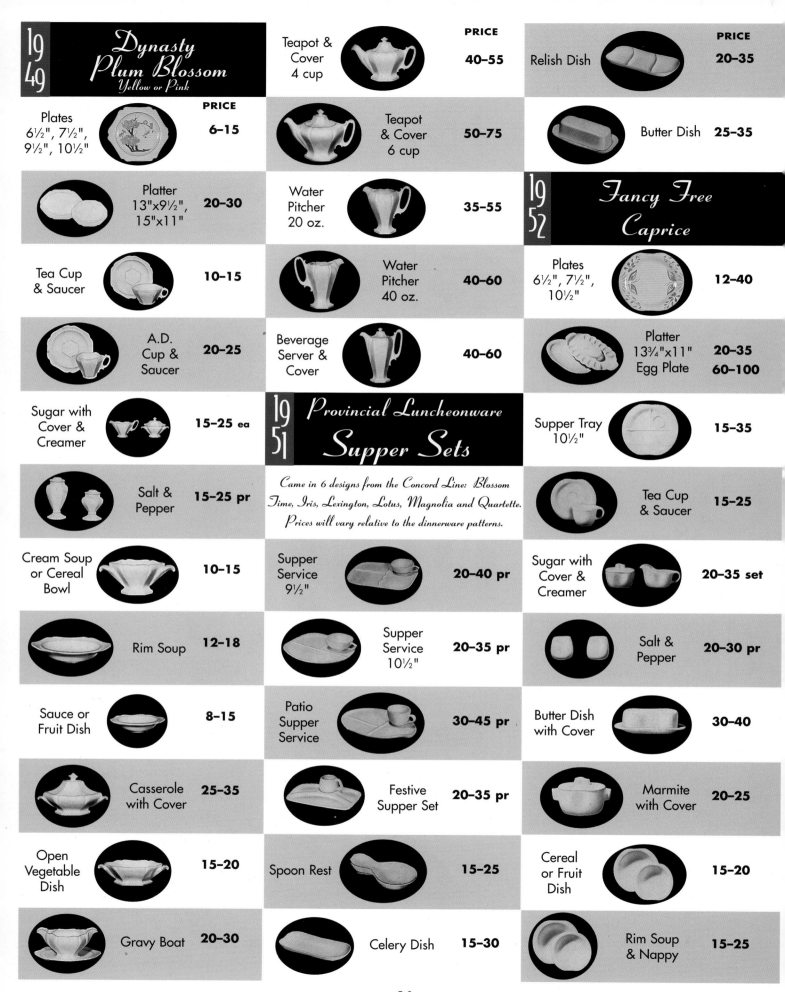

19 49 — Dynasty Plum Blossom
Yellow or Pink

Item		Price
Plates 6½", 7½", 9½", 10½"		6–15
Platter 13"x9½", 15"x11"		20–30
Tea Cup & Saucer		10–15
A.D. Cup & Saucer		20–25
Sugar with Cover & Creamer		15–25 ea
Salt & Pepper		15–25 pr
Cream Soup or Cereal Bowl		10–15
Rim Soup		12–18
Sauce or Fruit Dish		8–15
Casserole with Cover		25–35
Open Vegetable Dish		15–20
Gravy Boat		20–30

Item		Price
Teapot & Cover 4 cup		40–55
Teapot & Cover 6 cup		50–75
Water Pitcher 20 oz.		35–55
Water Pitcher 40 oz.		40–60
Beverage Server & Cover		40–60

19 51 — Provincial Luncheonware
Supper Sets

Came in 6 designs from the Concord Line: Blossom Time, Iris, Lexington, Lotus, Magnolia and Quartette. Prices will vary relative to the dinnerware patterns.

Item		Price
Supper Service 9½"		20–40 pr
Supper Service 10½"		20–35 pr
Patio Supper Service		30–45 pr
Festive Supper Set		20–35 pr
Spoon Rest		15–25
Celery Dish		15–30

Item		Price
Relish Dish		20–35
Butter Dish		25–35

19 52 — Fancy Free Caprice

Item		Price
Plates 6½", 7½", 10½"		12–40
Platter 13¾"x11"		20–35
Egg Plate		60–100
Supper Tray 10½"		15–35
Tea Cup & Saucer		15–25
Sugar with Cover & Creamer		20–35 set
Salt & Pepper		20–30 pr
Butter Dish with Cover		30–40
Marmite with Cover		20–25
Cereal or Fruit Dish		15–20
Rim Soup & Nappy		15–25

Item	PRICE
Divided Vegetable Dish & Relish Dish	20–30
Celery Dish and Pickle Dish	20–30
Gravy or Sauce Boat with Tray	30–45
Casserole with Cover	35–55
Teapot & Cover	55–85
Water Pitcher	40–60
Beverage Server with Cover	40–60

Fancy Free Desert

Item	PRICE
Plates 6½", 7½", 10½"	12–60
Platter 13¾"x11"	30–45
Egg Plate	90–120
Supper Tray 10½"	25–35
Tea Cup & Saucer	15–25
Sugar with Cover & Creamer	20–35 ea

Item	PRICE
Salt & Pepper	20–30 ea
Butter Dish with Cover	30–45
Marmite with Cover	30–40
Cereal or Fruit Dish	18–25
Rim Soup Dish & Nappy	20–30
Divided Vegetable Dish & Relish Dish	25–40
Celery Dish & Pickle Dish	25–40
Gravy or Sauce Boat with Tray	40–50
Casserole with Cover	45–60
Teapot & Cover	60–90
Water Pitcher	45–60
Beverage Server with Cover	60–80

Village Green

PATTERN	Plates 6", 8", 10"	Chop Plate 14" / Platters 13" & 15"	Cup & Saucer	Coffee Mug & Beverage Mug	Sugar with Cover & Creamer	Salt & Pepper	Butter Dish with Cover & Syrup Jug	Marmite & Handled Marmite	Cereal Bowl	Rim Soup Bowl	Individual Salad Bowl	Salad Bowl 9" & 1...
Delta Blue	15–125*	50–75	25–40	30–65 ea	35–60 set	50–60 pr	BD 35–50 SJ 35–65	20–30	15–20	20–35	25–40	50–9...
Picardy	8–18	30–40	12–15	15–20 ea	25–35 set	18–25 pr	BD 25–40 SJ 20–30	15–18	8–12	10–15	10–15	25–3...
Provincial	6–15	25–40	10–12	—	20–25 set	18–25 pr	BD 25–40 SJ 15–25	12–15	7–10	—	—	—
Two Step	8–18	30–40	12–15	15–20 ea	25–35 set	18–25 pr	BD 25–40 SJ 20–30	15–18	8–12	10–15	10–15	25–35
Village Brown	6–15	25–40	10–12	10–15 ea	18–25 set	18–25 pr	BD 25–40 SJ 15–25	12–15	7–10	8–12	10–15	20–30
Village Green	6–15	30–45	10–12	12–16 ea	25–30 set	18–25 pr	BD 25–40 SJ 20–30	12–15	10–15	15–18	18–25	35–5...

*Delta Blue plates are valued much higher than the rest of the line, estimated up to $240 each, because many people collect only plates.

Village Green and Village Brown

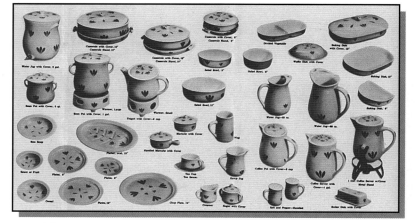

Village Green

	getable Dish	Divided Vegetable Dish	Sauce or Fruit Dish	Gravy Boat with Tray	Baking Dish with Cover 6" & 12"	Casserole with Cover & Stand 1 qt., 2 qt., 4 qt.	Bean Pot with Warmer 2 qt., 4 qt.	Teapot & Cover	Water Pitcher 4 cup, 10 cup	1 Gallon Coffee Server with Stand	2 Gallon Water Jar	Beverage Server & Cover	PATTERN
	5–50	35–45	15–25	50–85	25–45	60–110 Stand 30–40	40–75 Warmer 30–40	60–100	65–95	90–125	225–350	45–70	Delta Blue
	0–25	20–25	10–15	30–50	18–30	35–50	25–30 Warmer 20–25	50–75	35–50	60–80	—	35–50	Picardy
	8–25	—	8–12	—	—	Different style than above. See catalog page below. 25–40	30–40	50–65	35–50	—	—	—	Provincial
	0–25	20–25	10–15	30–50	18–30	35–50	25–30 Warmer 20–25	50–75	35–50	60–80	—	35–50	Two Step
	8–25	18–25	8–12	25–40	18–25	25–40 Stand 20–30	20–25 Warmer 30–40	50–65	35–50	50–65	150–225	35–50	Village Brown
	5–30	20–25	10–15	35–50	18–30	35–60 Stand 25–35	25–45 Warmer 25–30	50–75	35–50	75–95	150–225	35–50	Village Green

SHAPE

Picardy

Provincial

Two-Step

SHAPE

PATTERN	Plates 10½", 7½", 6½"	Platters 13" & 15"	Egg Plate	Tea Cup & Saucer	Sugar with Cover & Creamer	Salt & Pepper	Butter Dish with Cover	Spoon Rest	Bread Tray	Cereal	Rim Soup	Sala Bowl 5½" 10½"
Capistrano	9–18	18–30	50–75	10–15	12–20 ea	15–20 pr	20–30	15–20	25–35	9–12	10–15	10–3
Country Garden	10–25	20–35	70–90	15–20	18–25 ea	18–25 pr	35–45	18–25	30–40	10–15	15–18	15–4
Driftwood	8–15	15–30	50–75	10–15	12–20 ea	15–20 pr	20–25	10–15	25–35	9–12	10–15	10–3
Midnight Rose	10–25	25–40	70–90	15–25	20–25 ea	25–35 pr	35–45	20–25	35–50	15–20	18–22	18–5
Pink Spice	10–25	20–35	70–90	15–20	18–25 ea	18–25 pr	35–45	18–25	30–40	10–15	15–18	15–4
Tweed Tex	6–15	15–25	35–40	10–12	10–12 ea	10–15 pr	20–25	10–15	15–20	8–10	9–12	10–2

...for the woman of taste

Capistrano.... an original, handpainted design depicting the graceful dip of a yellow-breasted, jet black bird into colorful, fruited foliage ... the lovely colors of the pattern pointed up by soft, sage green holloware in contrasting "basket-weave" texture.

Seldom does one pattern appeal to such a variety of tastes and needs as this beloved RED WING design. *Capistrano* is the choice of young brides-to-be who want their first set of dinnerware to be something very special ... of clever hostesses who choose their pattern with an eye to originality and color-versatility ... of smart homemakers who look for durability and practicality along with pleasing design ...

Like all RED WING dinnerware, *Capistrano* is oven proof and color fast, with design sealed under the glaze to prevent soap and detergent fading. Be sure you see it before you select your new pattern!

Capistrano

by RED WING

Country Garden

THE RED WING POTTERIES, Inc.
RED WING, MINNESOTA

Tweed-Tex

THE RED WING POTTERIES, INC.
RED WING, MINNESOTA

SHAPE

Divided Vegetable Dish	Sauce or Fruit Dish	Celery Dish	Nappy	Buffet Bowl	Gravy Boat	Soup Tureen with Cover	Casserole with Cover	Trivet	Teapot & Cover	Water Pitcher	Beverage Server & Cover	PATTERN
-25	8–12	15–25	15–20	20–35	15–25	30–40	25–30	25–30	60–80	30–45	40–60	Capistrano
-25	10–15	20–25	20–25	35–40	20–30	45–60	35–45	—	70–90	40–60	50–75	Country Garden
-25	8–12	15–25	15–20	20–35	15–25	30–35	20–25	—	60–80	40–60	40–60	Driftwood
-30	12–18	25–30	25–30	40–50	25–35	50–65	40–50	—	75–95	50–75	60–85	Midnight Rose
-25	10–15	20–25	20–25	30–45	20–30	45–60	35–45	—	70–90	40–60	50–75	Pink Spice
-20	6–8	15–20	10–15	18–22	12–18	25–30	20–25	—	45–50	25–30	30–35	Tweed Tex

Midnight Rose

THE RED WING POTTERIES, Inc.
RED WING MINNESOTA

Pink Spice

THE RED WING POTTERIES, Inc
RED WING, MINNESOTA

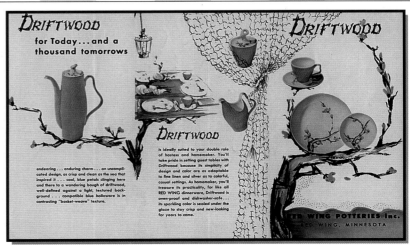

DRIFTWOOD for Today...and a thousand tomorrows

DRIFTWOOD

DRIFTWOOD

is ideally suited to your double role of hostess and homemaker. You'll take pride in setting guest tables with Driftwood because its simplicity of design and color are as adaptable to fine linen and silver as to colorful, casual settings. As homemaker, you'll treasure its practicality, for like all RED WING dinnerware, Driftwood is oven-proof and dishwasher-safe... its sparkling color is sealed under the glaze to stay crisp and new-looking for years to come.

endearing ... enduring charm ... an uncomplicated design, as crisp and clean as the sea that inspired it . . . cool, blue petals clinging here and there to a wandering bough of driftwood, well-defined against a light, textured background . . . compatible blue holloware is in contrasting "basket-weave" texture.

RED WING POTTERIES, Inc.
RED WING, MINNESOTA

Casual

SHAPE / PATTERN	Plates 6½", 7½", 10½"	Platters 13", 20" (with stand)*	Tray 24"	Cocktail Tray	Cup & Saucer	Sugar with Cover & Creamer	Salt & Pepper	Butter Dish with Cover	Butter Warmer with Cover (and stand)*	Handled Marmite with Cover	Rim Soup Bowl	Individual Salad Bowl 5½"
Bob White	6–12	30–65	45–75	35–50	6–10	30–45 set	25–35 pr	25–40	40–50	15–25	15–20	8–12
Hearthside	10–25	35–60	50–90	35–50	12–15	30–50 set	35–50 pr	30–45	40–50	20–30	15–20	10–15
Round-Up or Chuck Wagon**	30–60 CW 125	75–150	125–150	55–75	60–80	65–90 set	75–100 pr	60–85	65–95	60–75	35–50	35–45
Smart Set	10–30	45–75	75–90	50–70	25–30	50–70 set	35–50 pr	45–75	45–75	25–30	20–30	12–20
Tip-Toe	6–12	25–40	45–55	35–45	6–10	20–25 set	18–25 pr	20–25	25–35	15–20	10–12	7–10

*Prices given do not include stands. Add 25–35% to the price for pieces with the stand.

**Chuck Wagon motif is similar. Chuck Wagon plates do not have a chuck wagon image on them.

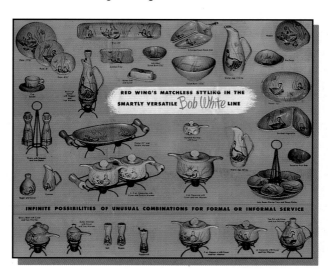

SHAPE

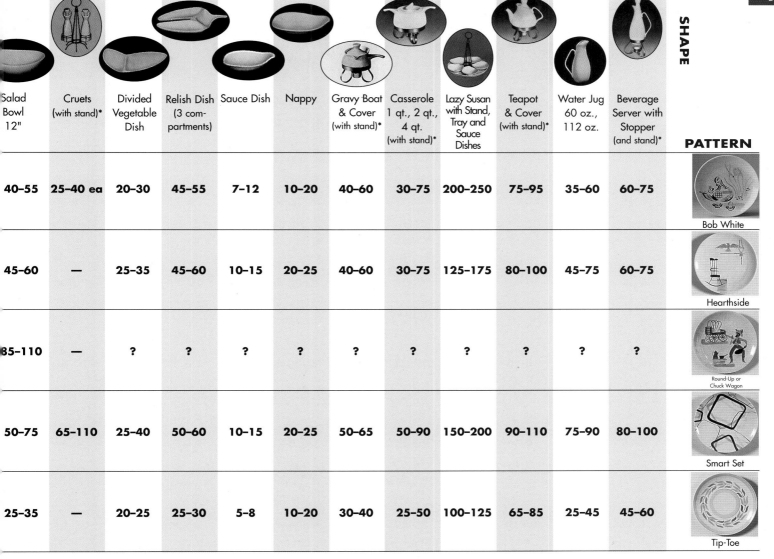

Salad Bowl 12"	Cruets (with stand)*	Divided Vegetable Dish	Relish Dish (3 compartments)	Sauce Dish	Nappy	Gravy Boat & Cover (with stand)*	Casserole 1 qt., 2 qt., 4 qt. (with stand)*	Lazy Susan with Stand, Tray and Sauce Dishes	Teapot & Cover (with stand)*	Water Jug 60 oz., 112 oz.	Beverage Server with Stopper (and stand)*	PATTERN
40–55	25–40 ea	20–30	45–55	7–12	10–20	40–60	30–75	200–250	75–95	35–60	60–75	Bob White
45–60	—	25–35	45–60	10–15	20–25	40–60	30–75	125–175	80–100	45–75	60–75	Hearthside
85–110	—	?	?	?	?	?	?	?	?	?	?	Round-Up or Chuck Wagon
50–75	65–110	25–40	50–60	10–15	20–25	50–65	50–90	150–200	90–110	75–90	80–100	Smart Set
25–35	—	20–25	25–30	5–8	10–20	30–40	25–50	100–125	65–85	25–45	45–60	Tip-Toe

*Prices given do not include stands. Add 25–35% to the price for pieces with the stand.

HEARTHSIDE

Tip Toe by *Red Wing*

RED WING POTTERIES, INC.

The versatility of the entire line gives you completeness, style, with great possibilities of unusual combinations.

Smart Set
RED WING POTTERY

Futura

PATTERN	Plates 6½", 8½", 10½"	Platter 13", 15"	Tea Cup & Saucer	Coffee Mug	Sugar with Cover	Creamer	Salt & Pepper	Butter Dish with Cover	Cereal Bowl	Rim Soup Bowl	Salad Bowl 12"
Colonnes	8–25	25–35	10–15	—	15–25	15–25	20–30 pr	20–30	10–15	12–18	30–40
Crazy Rhythm	6–15	25–35	10–20	—	20–25	20–25	20–30 pr	20–30	12–18	15–20	30–40
Frontenac	6–15	25–35	10–15	—	15–25	15–25	20–30 pr	20–30	10–15	12–18	30–40
Golden Viking	6–15	20–30	10–15	—	15–25	15–25	20–30 pr	20–30	10–15	12–18	30–40
Lupine	6–15	20–30	10–15	—	15–25	15–25	20–30 pr	20–30	10–15	12–18	30–40
Montmartre	10–25	35–45	20–30	—	30–40	25–30	25–35 pr	25–35	15–20	15–20	35–45
Northern Lights	8–18	20–30	10–15	—	15–25	15–25	20–30 pr	20–30	10–15	12–18	30–40
Random Harvest	8–18	25–35	15–18	—	20–25	20–30	25–35 pr	25–35	12–18	15–20	35–45
Red Wing Rose	6–15	20–30	10–15	—	15–25	15–25	20–30 pr	20–30	10–15	12–18	25–30
Tampico	8–20	25–35	15–18	20–25	20–25	20–30	20–30 pr	25–35	12–18	15–20	30–40

Divided Vegetable Dish	Relish Dish	Sauce or Fruit Dish	Nappy	Gravy Boat with Tray	Casserole with Cover	Teapot & Cover	Water Pitcher 1 qt.	Water Pitcher 2 qt.	Beverage Server & Cover	SHAPE PATTERN
20–25	18–25	8–10	15–20	35–40	35–50	75–95	40–50	50–75	60–85	Colonnes
20–25	18–25	8–10	15–20	35–40	35–50	75–95	40–50	50–75	60–85	Crazy Rhythm
20–25	18–25	8–10	15–20	30–35	35–50	75–95	40–50	50–75	50–75	Frontenac
20–25	18–25	8–10	15–20	30–35	35–50	75–95	40–50	50–75	60–85	Golden Viking
20–25	18–25	8–10	15–20	30–35	35–50	75–95	40–50	50–75	50–75	Lupine
30–35	20–25	10–15	25–30	35–45	50–75	85–110	50–65	75–110	75–110	Montmartre
20–25	18–25	8–10	15–20	30–35	35–50	75–95	40–50	50–75	60–85	Northern Lights
25–30	18–25	8–10	15–20	35–45	45–65	85–100	40–60	65–95	65–95	Random Harvest
20–25	18–25	8–10	15–20	30–35	35–50	65–80	35–45	50–75	50–75	Red Wing Rose
25–30	18–25	10–12	18–25	35–45	50–75	50–75	40–60	65–95	65–95	Tampico

BEIGE...
the basic color of Moderns

CRAZY RHYTHM ...a subtle abstract design traced in rich browns, dotted with mustard-gold, on a beige fleck background.

stunning simplicity... in perfect accord with the varying moods of Moderns, going from outdoor barbeque to festive buffet to candelabra affairs with ease... fast becoming a favorite with brides who want their first set of dinnerware to be something very, very special.

for generations... RED WING dinnerware has been known and admired for its fashion leadership. Each design is original... handpainted... tastefully styled to help you express your own personality in a variety of striking table arrangements.

CRAZY RHYTHM
BY RED WING

MODERN ... from the imaginative design, "futura" shape, and subtle colors to its wonderful oven-to-table-to-dishwasher versatility.

...inviting as a cool mountain brook on a summer day

Lupine BY RED WING
...for your family's and guests' dining pleasure.

Lupine a serenely, subdued pattern with a quaint charm to endure and endear through the years. A table setting to reflect your genuine cordiality. The internationally-favored, floral motif, hand painted in delicate yellow and soft gray.

Oven proof and color fast ...and like all RED WING dinnerware is detergent-safe... colors will stay bright and new looking despite years of constant use.

Designed by Charles Murphy

See center spread for the complete list of Lupine available in the Futura shape.

...a new look for your table

It's fiesta time every time you dine on this exciting new RED WING dinnerware, handpainted in rich browns, greens, and vivacious melon accents, lightly flecked with brown overall. Tampico... a pattern to pep up that 3-times-a-day routine... to make all your entertaining colorful and different.

...the life of the party!

If dinnerware could dance, Tampico would surely outstep them all! Set your table with this vivacious dinnerware, and ...suddenly it's a party!...whether you're serving 'burgers backyard style or snacking on TV tables.

Like all RED WING dinnerware, Tampico is oven proof and color fast... the delightful design sealed under the glaze to stay like new through years of festive dining.

RED WING'S Tampico
different! festive! colorful! ...the new "South of the Border" look in dinnerware

Buffet Royale
A MODERN SERVICE ENSEMBLE BOTH FUNCTIONAL AND IMAGINATIVE!

Red Wing Potteries' Classic, Exciting, new Buffet Royale. We know of nothing like it ... nothing to match Royale for design, for functionality. Matte-white pottery pieces are completely oven safe. Service stands in black walnut finish are sturdy and handsome in their own right.

PRICE LIST
JANUARY 1960

	Price	Price With Stand
Large salad bowl	$ 4.00	$
Salt and pepper, pair	4.00	
Sugar	3.50	
Creamer	2.50	
Bread tray	6.00	
2 qt. casserole with cover	7.00	14.95
Beverage server with cover	7.00	14.95
Divided vegetable with two covers	14.00	24.95
Platter with dome	14.00	24.95
Two 2 qt. casseroles		24.95
Casserole and beverage server with covers		24.95

RED WING POTTERIES, Inc.
RED WING, MINNESOTA

Red Wing's Contemporary
Hand Decorated Ovenware
White with Turquoise

RED WING'S
Contemporary
OVEN PROOF

For Kitchen - For Oven - For Serving
From Kitchen to Oven to Table

Color Fast - Oven Proof

January, 1956

	Each
Salt and Pepper	$ 4.00
Casserole with Cover, 1½ qt.	5.00
Casserole with Cover, 2½ qt.	6.00
Water Pitcher, 2 qt.	4.50
Salad Bowl, 12"	6.00
Marmite with Cover	3.00
Bean Pot with Cover and Handle, 2 qt.	6.50
Bean Pot with Cover and Handle, 4 qt.	8.00
Munch Jar	5.50
Canister, Small	4.00
Canister, Medium	4.50
Canister, Large or Cookie Jar	5.50

These items are individually boxed.

The Red Wing Potteries, Inc., Red Wing, Minn.

THE RED WING POTTERIES, Inc.
RED WING, MINNESOTA

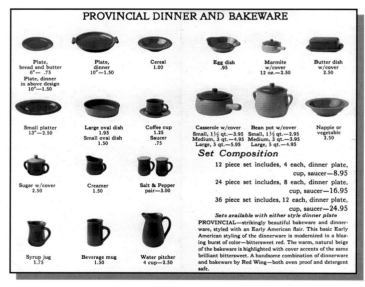

PROVINCIAL DINNER AND BAKEWARE

Item	Price
Plate, bread and butter 6"—	.75
Plate, dinner 10"—	1.50
Plate, dinner in above design 10"—	1.50
Cereal	1.00
Egg dish	.95
Marmite w/cover 12 oz.—	2.50
Butter dish w/cover	2.50
Small platter 13"—	2.50
Large oval dish	1.95
Small oval dish	1.50
Coffee cup	1.25
Saucer	.75
Nappie or vegetable	2.50
Sugar w/cover	2.50
Creamer	1.50
Salt & Pepper pair—	3.00
Syrup jug	1.75
Beverage mug	1.50
Water pitcher 4 cup—	2.50

Casserole w/cover Small, 1½ qt.—3.95 Medium, 3 qt.—4.95 Large, 5 qt.—5.95

Bean pot w/cover Small, 1½ qt.—3.95 Medium, 3 qt.—3.95 Large, 5 qt.—4.95

Set Composition
12 piece set includes, 4 each, dinner plate, cup, saucer—8.95
24 piece set includes, 8 each, dinner plate, cup, saucer—16.95
36 piece set includes, 12 each, dinner plate, cup, saucer—24.95

Sets available with either style dinner plate

PROVINCIAL—strikingly beautiful bakeware and dinnerware, styled with an Early American flair. This basic Early American styling of the dinnerware is modernized in a blazing burst of color—bittersweet red. The warm, natural beige of the bakeware is highlighted with cover accents of the same brilliant bittersweet. A handsome combination of dinnerware and bakeware by Red Wing—both oven proof and detergent safe.

Continental Buffet
DRAMATIC BUFFET-SERVICE PIECES
by RED WING

color fast • tarnish free • oven proof

	Price	With Stand
Salad Bowl with Fork and Spoon		$
Salt and Pepper Shakers		
Sauce Boat with Cover and Stand		22.00
2 Quart Casserole with Stand		30.00
Beverage Server with Stand		26.00
Sugar Bowl with Cover		
Matching Creamer		
Double Casserole with Cover and Stand		42.50
Platter with Dome Cover and Stand		36.00
16 Pc. Set—Charcoal		14.95

In White or Blue, with a smart, modern matte-finish glaze. Completely oven-proof. Warmer stands nickle-plated, tarnish free, require no special care.

Charles Murphy, Designer

The shape of the future is featured in these smart, modern servers. Gently curving contours make each piece a joy to handle. Sure-grip handles on the beverage server and cream pitcher make use a real pleasure.

RED WING POTTERIES, Inc.
RED WING, MINNESOTA

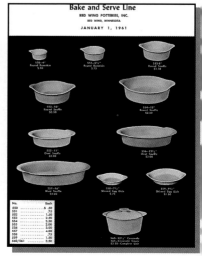

Bake and Serve Line
RED WING POTTERIES, INC.
RED WING, MINNESOTA

JANUARY 1, 1961

No.	Each
550	.50
551	.75
552	1.00
553	1.50
554	2.50
555	3.50
556	3.00
557	4.00
558	.75
559	1.50
560/561	3.50

26

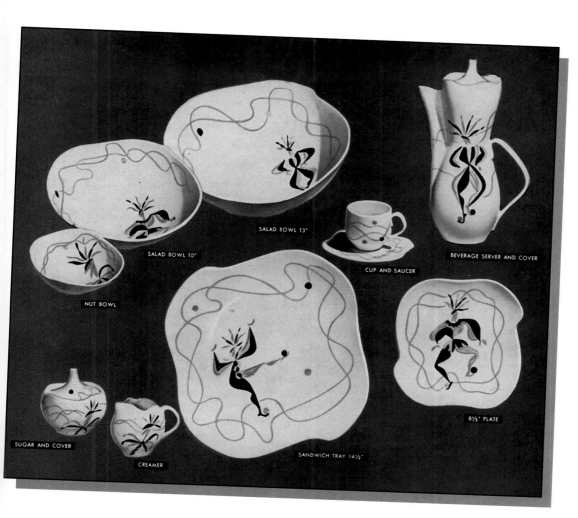

NUT BOWL

SALAD BOWL 10"

SALAD BOWL 13"

CUP AND SAUCER

BEVERAGE SERVER AND COVER

SUGAR AND COVER

CREAMER

SANDWICH TRAY 14½"

8½" PLATE

Merrileaf

Granada

HAND PAINTED IN
SOFT TONES OF BROWN,
YELLOW AND BURNT ORANGE

CHINA BY RED WING
Hand Painted - Color Fast - Oven Proof
Detergent Safe

JANUARY 1963

	Each
Plate, 6", B&B	$1.20
Plate, 7", Salad	1.55
Plate, 10", Dinner	2.50
Cup	1.85
Saucer	1.10
Sauce or Fruit	1.20
Cereal Salad Soup	1.75
Sugar with Cover	3.50
Creamer	2.50
Salt and Pepper, pair	3.00
Vegetable Dish	3.75
Divided Vegetable	5.50
Salad Bowl, Large	6.95
Butter Dish with Cover	4.00
Platter, Small	4.95
Platter, Large	6.50
Casserole with Cover	8.95
Teapot with Cover	6.50
Beverage Server with Cover	8.95
Gravy Boat with Cover	6.50
Celery, 16"	3.50
Bread Tray, 19"	5.00
Ash Tray	.75

Sets

4 Piece Place Setting .... $ 5.50
One each 7" plate, 10" plate, cup, saucer.

16 Piece Set: Service for 4 .... 19.95
Four each 7" plate, 10" plate, cup, saucer.

45 Piece Set: Service for 8 .... 64.95
Eight each 7" plate, 10" plate, cup, saucer, cereal. One each sugar and cover, creamer, nappie, small platter.

RED WING POTTERIES, Inc.
RED WING, MINNESOTA

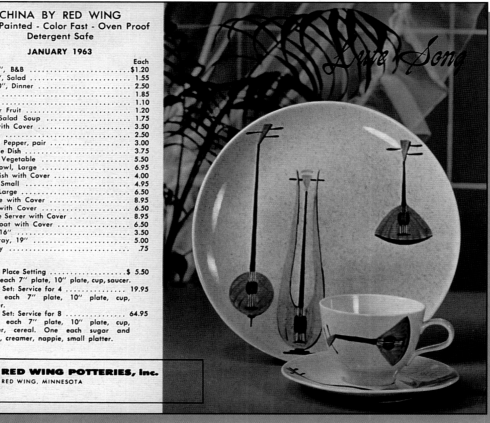

Love Song

Mediterrania

HAND PAINTED IN
LOVELY FLORAL DESIGN
OF BLUE AND GREEN TONES

Vintage

HAND PAINTED IN
SOFT GREYS AND
LIGHT ORCHID

1956 — Spruce — White and Turquoise (Contemporary Line)

Item	Price
Plates* 6½", 8", 10½"	15–35
Platter* 15"	30–50
Tea Cup & Saucer*	20–30
Sugar*	30–35
Creamer*	30–35
Salt & Pepper	50–85 pr
Marmite with Cover	45–60
Cereal, Salad or Soup Bowl	25–35
Salad Bowl	75–95
Casserole with Cover 1½ qt., 2 qt.	85–125
Bean Pot with Cover and Handle 2 qt., 4 qt.	100–150
Munch Jar	95–125

(Canister group)

Item	Price
Canister (Small & Medium)	95–125 ea
Canister (Large) or Cookie Jar	100–135
Water Pitcher	95–125

1956 — Continental Buffet

Item	Price
Platter with Dome-Cover and Stand	65–95
Sugar with Cover	18–25
Creamer	15–20
Salt & Pepper	18–25 pr
Salad Bowl with Fork & Spoon	60–75
Sauce Boat with Cover and Stand	30–45
2 Quart Casserole with Stand	40–60
Double Casserole with Cover and Stand	50–75
Beverage Server and Stand	50–75

1957 — Kermis

Item	Price
Plate 8½"	75–100
Sandwich Tray	100–135
Cup & Saucer	40–60
Sugar	40–60
Creamer	40–60
Nut Bowl	75–100
Salad Bowl 10", 13"	125–175
Beverage Server with Cover	125–175

1960 — Buffet Royale

Item	Price
Platter with Dome-Cover and Stand	65–95
Bread Tray	40–60
Sugar with Cover	18–25

*Available only in Spruce

	PRICE				
Creamer	15–20	Two 2 qt. Casseroles with Covers	75–90 set	Oval Soufflé 11"	10–15

 Salt & Pepper **20–30 pr**

19 63 Bake and Serve

Oval Soufflé 13½" 	15–25

			PRICE		
 Large Salad Bowl	30–40	Round Ramekin 4"	4–5	Oval Soufflé 16" 	25–35
Divided Vegetable Dish with two Covers and Stand	60–85	Round Ramekin 5½"	5–6	Shirred Egg Dish 7½"	8–12
2 qt. Casserole with Cover and Stand	50–75	Round Soufflé 8"	10–12	Shirred Egg Dish 9½"	10–15
Beverage Server with Cover and Stand	50–75	Round Soufflé 10"	10–15	Casserole with Cover 10½"	25–30
 Casserole and Beverage Server with Covers and Stand	85–110 set	Round Soufflé 13"	15–25		

BUFFET SERVICE

Contemporary

SPRUCE

FOR THE KITCHEN, OVEN AND TABLE

Plate - 10½" Plate - 8" Plate - 6½"

Sugar & Cover   Creamer   Cup & Saucer   Platter - 15"   Bowl (Cereal Salad-Soup)

4 qt. Bean Pot   2 qt. Bean Pot   Range Salt & Pepper   Marmite   1½ Qt. Casserole   2½ Qt. Casserole

Salad Bowl 12"   Canister Jar 1 Qt.   Canister Jar 2 Qt.   Canister Jar 2½ Qt.   Water Pitcher 2 Qt.   Munch Jar

True China

PATTERN	Plates 10½", 7½", 6½"	Platter (Small & Large)	Cup & Saucer	Creamer	Sugar with Cover	Salt & Pepper	Butter Dish with Cover	Bread Tray	Cereal Bowl	Large Salad Bowl
Crocus	8–18	25–40	15–20	15–20	18–25	20–30 pr	25–40	35–55	10–15	35–50
Daisy Chain	8–25	20–35	10–15	10–15	10–15	18–25 pr	25–40	25–40	8–12	20–30
Granada	8–15	20–35	10–15	10–15	10–15	18–25 pr	25–40	25–40	8–12	20–30
Lute Song	8–15	20–30	10–12	10–15	10–15	15–18 pr	20–30	20–35	8–11	20–30
Majestic	8–15	20–30	10–12	10–15	10–15	12–18 pr	15–25	20–35	7–10	20–25
Mediterrania	8–18	25–40	15–20	15–20	18–25	18–25 pr	25–40	35–55	10–15	35–50
Merrileaf	8–18	25–40	15–20	15–20	18–25	18–25 pr	25–40	35–55	10–15	35–50
Vintage	10–20	25–40	18–25	20–25	25–30	20–30 pr	30–45	45–75	12–18	45–60

										SHAPE
Vegetable Dish	Divided Vegetable Dish	6-piece Relish Dish	Sauce or Fruit Dish	Celery Dish	Gravy Boat with Cover	Casserole with Cover	Ash Tray	Teapot & Cover	Beverage Server & Cover	PATTERN
20–35	25–35	50–85	8–12	18–25	30–45	45–60	12–20	50–75	60–85	Crocus
20–25	20–25	45–75	6–10	15–20	30–40	30–45	12–20	50–75	60–75	Daisy Chain
20–25	20–25	45–75	6–10	15–20	30–40	30–45	12–20	50–75	60–75	Granada
20–25	20–25	45–75	6–10	15–20	25–35	30–45	12–20	50–75	60–75	Lute Song
18–22	18–22	40–60	5–9	15–18	25–30	30–40	10–12	50–65	45–60	Majestic
20–35	25–35	50–85	8–12	18–25	30–45	45–60	12–20	50–75	60–75	Mediterrania
20–35	25–35	50–85	8–12	18–25	30–45	45–60	12–20	50–75	60–75	Merrileaf
25–35	30–40	75–100	10–15	20–28	45–60	50–75	12–20	85–110	70–95	Vintage

Duo—Tone (Cylinder)

SHAPE

PATTERN	Plates 6", 7", 10"	Platter 13", 15"	Cup & Saucer	A.D. Cup & Saucer	Sugar with Cover & Creamer	Salt & Pepper	Butter Dish with Cover	Bread Tray	Cereal, Salad or Soup Bowl	Salad Bowl 10"	Vegetable Dish
Desert Sun	6–12	20–30	7–10	15–20	15–25 pr	15–25 pr	25–35	40–60	15–18	30–45	20–25
Flight	30–80	60–90	40–60	60–80	75–95 pr	60–90 pr	60–80	75–100	60–80	70–90	70–90
Pepe	6–12	20–30	10–12	12–18	20–30 pr	20–25 pr	25–35	45–85	12–16	30–45	20–25
Pompeii	6–12	20–30	10–12	10–15	20–30 pr	18–25 pr	25–35	40–60	12–16	30–45	20–25
Tahitian Gold	5–10	18–25	7–10	10–12	20–30 pr	12–15 pr	20–25	25–35	8–12	20–30	15–25
Turtle Dove	6–12	20–30	10–12	10–15	20–30 pr	18–25 pr	25–35	40–60	12–16	30–45	20–25

SHAPE

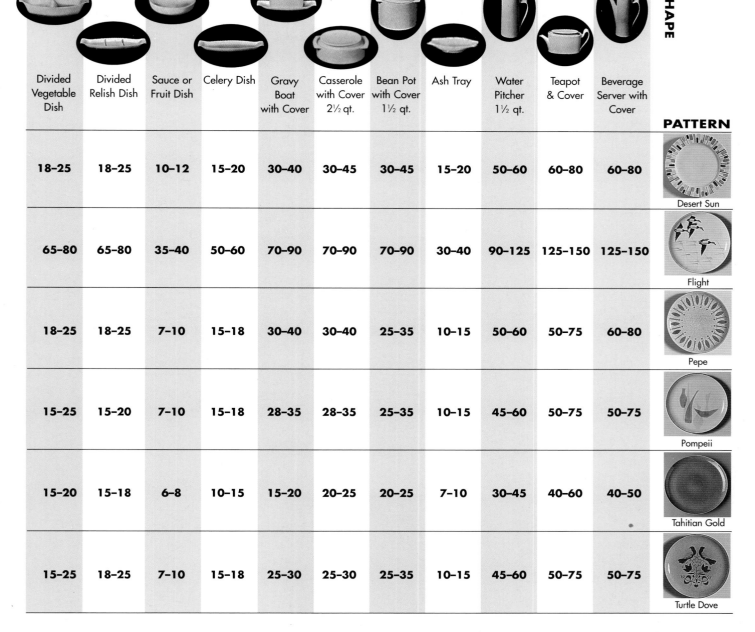

Divided Vegetable Dish	Divided Relish Dish	Sauce or Fruit Dish	Celery Dish	Gravy Boat with Cover	Casserole with Cover 2½ qt.	Bean Pot with Cover 1½ qt.	Ash Tray	Water Pitcher 1½ qt.	Teapot & Cover	Beverage Server with Cover	PATTERN
18–25	18–25	10–12	15–20	30–40	30–45	30–45	15–20	50–60	60–80	60–80	Desert Sun
65–80	65–80	35–40	50–60	70–90	70–90	70–90	30–40	90–125	125–150	125–150	Flight
18–25	18–25	7–10	15–18	30–40	30–40	25–35	10–15	50–60	50–75	60–80	Pepe
15–25	15–20	7–10	15–18	28–35	28–35	25–35	10–15	45–60	50–75	50–75	Pompeii
15–20	15–18	6–8	10–15	15–20	20–25	20–25	7–10	30–45	40–60	40–50	Tahitian Gold
15–25	18–25	7–10	15–18	25–30	25–30	25–35	10–15	45–60	50–75	50–75	Turtle Dove

POMPEII

TURTLE DOVE

TAHITIAN GOLD

Like China

SHAPE PATTERN	Plates 6", 7", 10"	Platter (Small & Large)	Cup & Saucer	Sugar with Cover & Creamer	Salt & Pepper	Butter Dish with Cover	Bread Tray	Cereal, Salad or Soup Bowl	Vegetable Dish	Large Salad Bowl
Blue Shadow	5–10	15–20	8–10	15–25 set	10–15 pr	15–20	20–25	6–9	10–15	20–25
Brocade	5–12	18–25	10–12	25–35 set	10–15 pr	20–25	25–30	7–10	15–18	25–30
Damask	5–12	18–25	10–12	25–35 set	10–15 pr	20–25	25–30	7–10	15–18	25–35
Kashmir	7–15	20–35	12–15	35–45 set	15–18 pr	25–30	25–35	7–12	20–30	35–45

Blue Shadows by Red Wing

Brocade by Red Wing

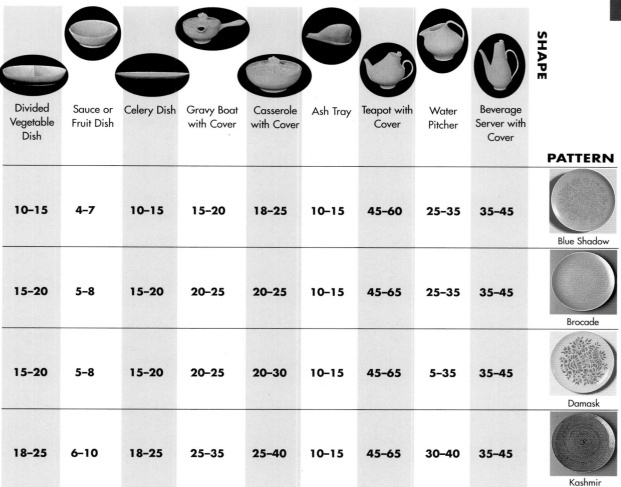

SHAPE	Divided Vegetable Dish	Sauce or Fruit Dish	Celery Dish	Gravy Boat with Cover	Casserole with Cover	Ash Tray	Teapot with Cover	Water Pitcher	Beverage Server with Cover	PATTERN
	10–15	4–7	10–15	15–20	18–25	10–15	45–60	25–35	35–45	Blue Shadow
	15–20	5–8	15–20	20–25	20–25	10–15	45–65	25–35	35–45	Brocade
	15–20	5–8	15–20	20–25	20–30	10–15	45–65	5–35	35–45	Damask
	18–25	6–10	18–25	25–35	25–40	10–15	45–65	30–40	35–45	Kashmir

Damask

Ceramastone

SHAPE → PATTERN ↓	Plates 6", 7", 10"	Platter 13" & 15"	Cup & Saucer	Sugar with Cover	Creamer	Salt & Pepper	Butter Dish with Cover	Cereal, Salad or Soup Bowl	Vegetable Dish	Oval Vegetable Dish
Adobestone	3–10	12–18	4–8	7–10	7–10	10–15 pr	10–15	3–8	10–12	10–12
Charstone Bleu	3–15	12–18	4–8	7–10	7–10	10–15 pr	10–15	3–8	10–12	10–12
Greenwichstone	3–10	12–18	4–8	7–10	7–10	10–15 pr	10–15	3–8	10–12	10–12
Hearthstone Beige	3–10	12–18	4–8	7–10	7–10	10–15 pr	10–15	3–8	10–12	10–12
Hearthstone Orange	3–10	12–18	4–8	7–10	7–10	10–15 pr	10–15	3–8	10–12	10–12
Heatherstone	3–20	12–18	4–8	7–10	7–10	10–15 pr	10–15	3–8	10–12	10–12

GREENWICHSTONE by Red Wing

RED WING POTTERIES, inc.
RED WING, MINNESOTA

HEARTHSTONE BEIGE by Red Wing

Sears

SHAPE

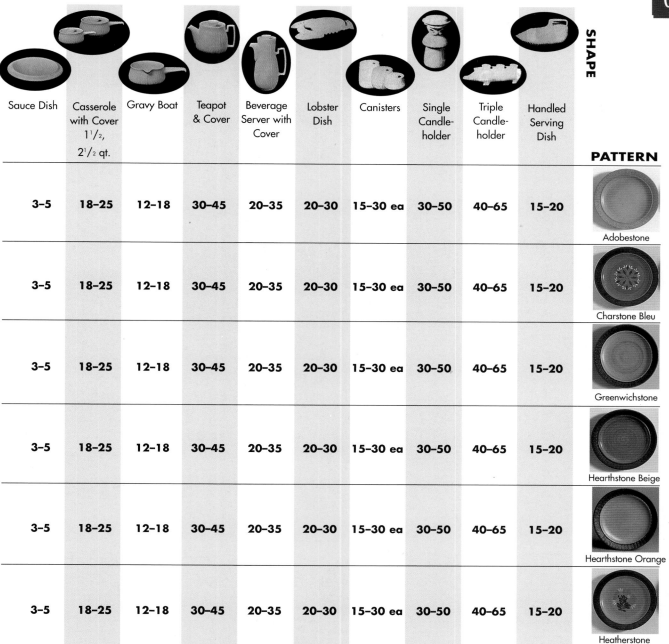

Sauce Dish	Casserole with Cover 1½, 2½ qt.	Gravy Boat	Teapot & Cover	Beverage Server with Cover	Lobster Dish	Canisters	Single Candle-holder	Triple Candle-holder	Handled Serving Dish	PATTERN
3–5	18–25	12–18	30–45	20–35	20–30	15–30 ea	30–50	40–65	15–20	Adobestone
3–5	18–25	12–18	30–45	20–35	20–30	15–30 ea	30–50	40–65	15–20	Charstone Bleu
3–5	18–25	12–18	30–45	20–35	20–30	15–30 ea	30–50	40–65	15–20	Greenwichstone
3–5	18–25	12–18	30–45	20–35	20–30	15–30 ea	30–50	40–65	15–20	Hearthstone Beige
3–5	18–25	12–18	30–45	20–35	20–30	15–30 ea	30–50	40–65	15–20	Hearthstone Orange
3–5	18–25	12–18	30–45	20–35	20–30	15–30 ea	30–50	40–65	15–20	Heatherstone

HEARTHSTONE ORANGE
by Red Wing

Sears

1964 — Hotel or Restaurant China

Item	Price
Plates 5⅜", 6⅜", 7⅜", 8¾", 9½"	3–9
Platters 8"x11", 9¼"x11½", 10¼"x12½"	10–18
Tea Cups	3–6
Coffee Cup & Saucer	3–8
Sugar	5–8
Creamer	5–10
Cereal or Salad Bowl 6½"	4–6
Soup Bowls 5", 5¾"	5–9
Sauce or Fruit Dish	3–5
Sauceboat	10–15
Bouillon Cup	3–5
Individual Teapot	15–25

Item	PRICE
Oval Bakers	8–12
Pot Pie Bowl	5–9
Lobster Dish	12–14
Ash Tray	4–6

1965 — Ebb Tide

Item	Price
Plates 6", 7", 10"	5–12
Platter	18–25
Cup without Handle & Saucer	15–25
Cup with Handle	5–8
Sugar & Creamer	15–30 set
Butter Dish with Cover	30–45
Cereal, Soup or Salad Bowl	10–15
Large Salad Bowl	20–35

Item	PRICE
Vegetable Dish	15–25
Sauce or Fruit Dish	5–10
Gravy Boat	20–30
Casserole with Cover	20–35

ebb tide
HAND PAINTED DINNERWARE BY RED WING

New, Vitrified
HOTEL or RESTAURANT
CHINA
by RED WING POTTERIES, Inc.
MAKERS OF FINE CERAMICS SINCE 1878

38

Specialty Items

Sweden House

Hamms Beer
"popcorn set"

A small quantity of pieces were made specially for the Hamms Brewery. They were decorated with the "land of sky blue water" motif on the Casual Line shapes of the water pitcher, large & small bowls, salt & peppers and some plates. Scarce.

Diamond Jims

Various pieces in both of these patterns are $10–40.

Pattern with garland motif
(Commonly refered to as "Wreath")

Most likely made in the mid-1930s (this assertion is based on the style of the Red Wing mark—a star surrounded by the words "Red Wing Potteries"). No documentation of this line has ever shown up, so the actual name of this pattern is a mystery. Other companies made this same style of dinnerware. Unmarked pieces should be matched to known Red Wing glazes from that era. Scarce.

One-of-a-Kind Pieces

One-of-a-kind pieces fall into two categories: "Lunch-hour Pieces" and experimental pieces. Workers would sometimes hand–decorate pieces for personal use. These were referred to as Lunch-hour Pieces because the workers theoretically would do them on their lunch hour. The example shown below was signed and dated on the back. All are considered rare.

B. PETERSDORF
DEC. 14 - 1948

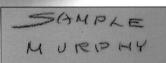

SAMPLE
MURPHY

The other category consists of official company tests or experimental pieces, such as the one above signed by Charles Murphy. All are considered rare.

Other rare items could be either lunch hour pieces or company tests, such as the clown bowls at left and the two plates above. The plates above use a Fondoso and a Chevron blank with an Orleans-style decoration. All are considered rare.